10 KiDS can SPoiL their parents

...and Increase Their Allowance

by
Roman & Ramsey Brown

illustrated by
Rich Davis

ISBN 1-881830-92-6

ABOUT THE AUTHORS

Roman and Ramsey are two talented and energetic boys who live in Arlington, Texas. Like most kids, they are involved in many activities including church, school programs, baseball, playing the drums, and just being boys. They are taught that greatness does not come by sitting on life's sidelines but by taking the snap and running with the ball.

Creativity and goal-setting have always been encouraged in their home, and the idea for this book sprang from a family dinner-table discussion. An overwhelming desire to travel to Disney World became an incentive to finish the project, get it published, and then take the trip as a fruit of their labor. They hope that readers will be inspired to believe in their own dreams and begin working toward their goals.

Children of all ages can read this book and use the ideas to express love to the parents who raise them and love them every day. Roman and Ramsey hope you and your family will laugh together and benefit from their suggestions as much as they did.

Enjoy it!

The Brown Family

CAUTION TO THE READER

Although the ideas expressed in this book really do work, we suggest you don't go too far to the extreme. Otherwise, you may set such a high standard that you will be under constant pressure to be your best all the time. No kid could possibly keep up this pace, and in fact, you just wouldn't be a kid if you did. So please don't try. The rest of us are counting on you. We kids have to stick together.

If you try these ideas and one of them backfires, quickly go on to the next one. This stuff really works and we have found that doing it actually makes you feel pretty good about yourself. Some of these things even work into adulthood. So keep this book handy at all times, and if you need a raise in your allowance, special privileges, or if you get into trouble, we suggest you start using our ideas right away.

Life is short so make yours count.

Ronan & Ramsey

#1
Tell your mom and dad that if you could have picked them, you would have (One of those "tug at your heart" things... use this one at just the right time)

#2
When you are on vacation, don't ask "are we there yet?" (This is a universal rule. Parents all get cranky after they hear this a few times...you are better off just going back to sleep)

1

#3

Teach your parents how to use the
computer (Just be sure you have a whole
day to waste and a lot of patience.
It's tough to teach an old dog
new tricks, you know)

Happy are those who find wisdom,
and those who get understanding.

PROVERBS 3:13 NRSV

3

#4

Always be polite and use your manners
(This will *never* work against you)

4

5

#5

Have pride in your family name. Live up to it

A good name is to be chosen rather than great riches, loving favor rather than silver and gold.

PROVERBS 22:1 NKJV

b

#6

Express your love by verbally telling them
every day "I love you Mom, I love you Dad"
(The key to making this work is
you gotta be believable)

#7

Help your mom go grocery shopping...
she will probably let you throw
in a few things for yourself

#8

Be your parents' best friend
(This really offers long-lasting rewards
for both of you)

9

#9

Make a cake on your mom's
and dad's birthday,
but don't mention their age
(They get real sensitive about this)

16

11

#10

When your mom drops something,
help pick it up for her
(She'll see you as such a
"fine young man...or lady")

All of you be of one mind,
having compassion for one another.

1 PETER 3:8 NKJV

12

#11
Get involved in family projects
(They love togetherness and teamwork)

#12
Take care of what you have and
don't complain about what you don't have
(This could ruin everything you
have been working for)

13

14

#13

Arm wrestle your dad, and let him win
(It's good for his ego and he will think
he's still "got it")

I can do all things through him
who strengthens me.

PHILIPPIANS 4:13 NRSV

15

#14
Wipe your feet clean before
coming into the house
(This will get you MAJOR brownie points)

16

17

#15

Communicate with your mom and dad.
You will all be happier
(With cell phones, pagers, and faxes,
communication shouldn't be a problem)

#16

Buy them a soda when you drag
them out on a hot day
(You can probably find some change
in your mom's or dad's car)

18

#17

Lead the family in the mealtime prayer
(But make sure no one is peeping)

Oh, give thanks to the Lord.

PSALM 106:1 NKJV

19

20

#78
Help your mother vacuum,
dust, and do household chores
(It's yukky stuff but someone's gotta do it)

#19

When your dad is gaining weight,
tell him...gently (It's that male ego thing)

They shall still bring forth fruit in old age;
they shall be fat and flourishing.

PSALM 92:14 KJV

23

#20

Remember to write to your grandparents
(More brownie points!!!)

#21

Encourage your dad in his job
(Tell him he can't quit yet,
there's still a lot of stuff you need)

24

#22

Spend time with them just being together
(A pro-family move that shows
them you are growing up)

25

#23

When your mom is on a diet,
tell her how thin she is looking
(Lots of points for this one)

Rejoice with those who rejoice,
and weep with those who weep.

ROMANS 12:15 NKJV

27

#24

Take out the trash without complaining
(Boy, this will really go over big)

29

#25

Leave your mom and dad hidden
"I love you" notes (They definitely will
save them forever and it might give you
some bargaining power when you need it)

#26

Ask your mom and dad "How was your day?"
(You need to sound sincere for this one to
work, so use a real good facial expression)

#27

Don't be selfish...EVER
(Not good)

Freely you have received, freely give.

MATTHEW 10:8 NKJV

31

32

#28

Help wash the dog
(We just throw ours in the pool...
this could be kind of fun)

33

#29

Encourage Family Night Out
and let them pick the place....
You could give them a hint or two
(such as bowling, the movies, etc.)

34

35

#30

Learn and quote for them some of life's lessons and virtues you have been taught.... If you don't remember more than one, you'd better study

36

#31
Shine your dad's shoes for him
(But don't charge him)

#32
Be a great example to others....
We need life heroes.

38

#33

Read to your mom and dad.
Perhaps an encouraging story
that will lift their spirits.
(Check the *Reader's Digest!*)

39

#34

Help your mother carry in the groceries
(She won't be able to refuse when you
ask for cookies and a Coke)

Let us not become weary in doing good.

GALATIANS 6:9 NIV

41

#35

Respect your parents and don't talk back
(Definitely don't talk back...this
could be a big deduction)

A soft answer turns away wrath.

PROVERBS 15:1 NKJV

#36

Draw them a picture.
It will make refrigerator headlines

42

#37

Keep your room clean...to a degree
CAUTION: DO NOT go overboard,
or they will come to expect it.
Dad says...
Cleanliness is next to godliness

43

44

#38

Save your money and take them out
to dinner.... Suggestion: the cafeteria
(They probably won't let you pay
but it's the thought that counts)

45

#39

Feed your pets and take care of
them like you promised you would.
Whose pets are they anyway?

46

#40

Never expect your mom and dad
to give you stuff (they don't owe you)
Instead, learn to be a giver yourself

It is more blessed to give than to receive.

ACTS 20:35 KJV

48

#41

Let them see you be a great
example to another kid
(Parents love this stuff, they'll think
their investment is finally paying off)

49

"Mom, Dad... Help is on the way!"

50

#42

Help take care of them when they're sick
(You might tell them you're willing
to stay home from school to help)

51

#43

Plant flowers in the garden for your mom
(just about any kind will do)

A child who gathers in summer is wise.

PROVERBS 10:5 PARAPHRASED

52

53

#44

Be understanding if your parents can't
go out and play with you all the time.
Sometimes they just get real tired
(They will be so relieved)

54

#45
Clean the table and help do the dishes...
as a rule of thumb
(And tell your mom dinner was great!)

#46
Tell your parents you need help
with your homework
(It makes them feel real important)

55

56

#47

Throw a surprise party for each of your parents on their birthday

#48

Wash the car with your dad...
get him soaking wet!!!!! (You might even
say something like "Gee Dad, I really
enjoy spending time with you")

59

#49

Be kind and considerate to your brother
or sister (This may be tough, but
it should pay off big!)

Let us love one another,
for love comes from God.

1 JOHN 4:7 NIV

60

#50

Brush your mom's hair for her
(Don't confuse her brush
with the dog's brush)

#51

Make hot chocolate in the winter,
while your dad gets the fire going

61

62

#52

Make them feel as special as they are

As we have opportunity, let us do good to all.

GALATIANS 6:10 NKJV

#53

Bring them breakfast in bed...
even if it is toast and cereal...
(Try not to burn the toast)

64

65

#54

Brag about your parents to
your friends (Surely you can find
something to brag about by now)

#55

Help your parents clean their room
(They get messy, too)

#56

Do your best at everything you do.
God expects it and so do they

Whatever work you do, do your best.
ECCLESIASTES 9:10 NCV

67

68

#57

Be there for your parents when they are hurting

Bear one another's burdens.

GALATIANS 6:2 NKJV

GT

#58

When they go out on a date,
tell your mom how pretty she is
and tell your dad how lucky he is

76

"Here's that dazzling couple, ladies and gentlemen!"

71

#59

Always open doors for your mother
(You have to open the door anyway...
so why not get credit for it?)

Be strong and do not let your hands be weak,
for your work shall be rewarded.

2 CHRONICLES 15:7 NKJV

#60

Create goals with your mom and dad
and accomplish them together

#61

Loan them some money when they are
broke. Don't worry, they probably
won't take it, but it sounds good

74

#62

Massage your poor mom's feet if she's real tired (She will think she died and went to heaven)

#63

If you have a swimming pool,
chip in to help keep it clean
(Don't throw frogs or goldfish in it)

76

#64

Have the kind of friends that
will make your parents proud
(Friends in gangs are not recommended)

A friend loves at all times.

PROVERBS 17:17 NKJV

78

#65

Share your day with your mom and dad
(You don't *have* to mention the food
fights or trouble at school)

#66

Pick wild flowers for your mom
(Try not to pick clover, it turns
brown too quickly)

THANKYOU!
Thankyou!
THANKS thankyou!
THANKYOU!
THANKS
THANKYOU!
Thankyou!

#67

Take every opportunity to say "Thank you"
(Parents can never hear this too much,
so make sure these two words are
part of your daily vocabulary)

A word fitly spoken is like apples of gold
in pictures of silver.

PROVERBS 25:11 KJV

81

#68

Imitate their good habits
(Flattery will get you everywhere)

82

83

#69

Tell them you are proud of them when they do good (Parents are like us kids, they need compliments, too, so they'll know they're on the right track)

#70

When your parents are bad, send them to their room and tell them it is called "tough love." Say something like "This hurts me more than it does you"

84

#71
Eat your fruits and vegetables
(They are supposed to be good for you)

#72

Bring them both a cup of
hot coffee in the morning
(It helps wake them up)

He who refreshes others
will himself be refreshed.

PROVERBS 11:25 NIV

#73

Keep a picture of your mom and dad
in your room (This goes over real big
'cause it warms their heart. It's another
one of those pro-family moves that
would be good for you to make)

88

#74

Let them sleep late when they are tired
(No music, no video games,
no loud cartoons)

90

#75

Understand that when your parents
punish you, it hurts them more than
it does you.... Yeah, right!!

A refusal to correct is a refusal to love.

PROVERBS 13:24 MSG

91

#76

Make their bed for them once in a while
(If you really need the points,
change the sheets, too!)

93

#77

Bring your dad his slippers after
a long, hard day (Perhaps even a cold glass
of iced tea. You'll see his mood change
right before your very eyes)

94

#78

Show them love...unconditionally
(Because unconditional love is such
a big deal these days)

#79

Always put things back where you
found them (We can never find the
scissors in our house)

Let all things be done decently and in order.
1 CORINTHIANS 14:40 KJV

96

#80

Watch old movies with them
like "It's a Wonderful Life" (It's in
black and white so it might be boring)
How many times have you heard this:
"You know, they just don't make movies
like they used to"

#81

Encourage them to go out and
be together for a change
(This usually gets us a pizza and a video)

97

98

#82

Sing to your mom and dad
(They love this stuff)

99

#83

Be a good student
(It's a reflection on them, you know)

Let the wise also hear and gain in learning.

PROVERBS 1:5 NRSV

100

101

#84

Take time to learn about your parents' hobbies and interests (as if you didn't already know)

#85

Invite them to school with you sometimes (It makes them proud when you show them off)

102

#86

Let sweetness come out of you...always
(This takes lots of practice...
but, hey, it could happen)

Say only what is good and helpful
to those you are talking to, and what
will give them a blessing.

EPHESIANS 4:29 TLB

109

1°4

#87

Make homemade birthday cards
(They always save these to
embarrass you later)

1°5

#88

Pray for them
(They need it a lot)

1 °6

#89

Help your dad do the yard work
(Only use this one in an emergency
or if you need a big raise)

In all labor there is profit.

PROVERBS 14:23 NKJV

108

#90

Love them, hug them, kiss them, and show affection (They will eat this up)

#91

Take responsibility for your own actions. Learn to say "I'm sorry" (Don't you hate it when this happens?)

109

UH... nice one, DAD...

110

#92

Take your dad fishing sometime
(However, if your fish is bigger
than his, throw it back)

A wise child makes a glad father.

//)

#*93*

Set the dinner table
(Especially if you plan on eating)

112

#94

Brainstorm with them about how to help other people (They like you to join in worthwhile causes)

#95

Tell them to keep your allowance once in a while (Warning: they will be shocked)

Do good, and lend, hoping for nothing in return; and your reward will be great.

LUKE 6:35 NKJV

114

#96

Show love and patience toward all God's creation (This is really tough for kids who love to shoot BB guns at birds, frogs, and lizards)

#97

Encourage your mom to stay home from work sometimes.... She might really like it and never go back!

115

"... Dad ?!"

116

#98

Occasionally buy them a gift,
just for the heck of it!
(This is so unlikely, it could be a problem,
so be careful how you explain it)

117

#99

Speak highly of your family wherever
you go (This doesn't mean to stand
on a ladder and speak, either)

Let your speech always be with grace.

COLOSSIANS 4:6 NKJV

118

119

#100

Do what you are asked to do
the first time without complaining
(Another big shocker....
Lots of points for this one)

Murmur not among yourselves.

JOHN 7:43 KJV

120

#101

The one we saved for last sort of sums
it all up for us: Thank God every day for
your mom and dad and always honor them.
We feel like everyone would be happier
if they did this, and God gave us
a promise for it:

Honor your father and mother, that you
may have a long, good life in the land
the Lord your God will give you.

EXODUS 20:12 TLB

THE END

NOW iT'S YOUR TURN!

If something good has happened to you after trying one or
more of these ideas, or if you have a story of how you spoil
your own parents, Roman and Ramsey would love to hear from you.

You can write to them in care of:

Garborg's, Inc.

P.O. Box 20132

Bloomington, MN 55420

or

garborg@compuserve.com